BBC Children's Books
Published by the Penguin Group
Penguin Books Ltd, 80 Strand, London, WC2R 0RL, England
Penguin Group (USA) Inc., 375 Hudson Street, New York 10014, USA
Penguin Books (Australia) Ltd, 250 Camberwell Road, Camberwell,
Victoria 3124, Australia
(A division of Pearson Australia Group PTY Ltd)
Penguin Group (NZ), 67 Apollo Drive, Rosedale, Auckland
0632, New Zealand (a division of Pearson New Zealand Ltd)
Canada, India, South Africa
Published by BBC Children's Books, 2011
Text and design © Children's Character Books
Pages 42-47 written by Colin Brake
Pages 18-23 written by Kieran Grant
Pages 29 and 36 written by Natasha Klus
Pages 10-17, 37 and 48-51 written by Moray Laing
Pages 18-23 and 42-47 coloured by James Offredi
Pages 9, 30-33, 38-39 and 52-55 written by Justin Richards
Pages 18-23 and 42-47 drawn by John Ross
Pages 24-28, 34-35, 40-41 written by Oli Smith
Pages 38-39 Illustrations by DuncanSmithStudio.com
Images on pages 10 and 11 courtesy of NASA
001 - 10 9 8 7 6 5 4 3 2 1
ISBN: 9781405907989
Printed in Italy

CONTENTS

The Legend CONTINUES...

They've saved the whole universe from certain destruction, now Amy and Rory are married and their adventures continue. But they share a secret — a secret so terrible they can't tell the Doctor what they've seen. Because, they've watched him die... As their own story as a married couple has only just begun, so it seems the Doctor's ancient and eventful story may be drawing to a close.

By the side of a lake in America, the Doctor meets an astronaut. Who or what is inside the spacesuit, no one knows — not yet. But whoever it is kills the Doctor — strikes him dead in front of his best friends, in front of Amy, Rory and River Song.

Amy and Rory don't have a lot of time to grieve, as their adventure in space and time continues. Together with the Doctor they must face the Silence in the United States of America. They must avoid the lure of the Siren on-board Captain Avery's pirate ship. They must face the Flesh.

In Amy's case, another adventure — another journey — is only just beginning. She is about to become a mother. But Rory knows nothing of that. He doesn't even realise that the Amy he has been travelling with isn't really Amy at all, but a synthetic doppelgänger, a double, a copy. When he and the Doctor discover the truth, then nothing stops them from finding and saving Amy. Not even an entire Cyber fleet.

They might have saved the universe, but saving their friends — saving each other — is the most important thing for the Doctor, Amy and Rory. And that makes it all the more difficult for Amy and Rory to keep their secret. They know that despite anything they can do, the Doctor will die. They know, because they have seen it happen...

Despite the sadness, the time travellers know that they are on the most wonderful adventure. They are having the time of their lives. Perhaps having seen the TARDIS itself become a living person for a while has heightened their sense of adventure, of the impossible.

As well as each other, they have so many friends they can count on – strange and wonderful people and aliens they have met on their many travels. From Madame Vastra, the Victorian Silurian to Commander Strax, the Sontaran medic, from pirate Captain Avery and his crew to Dorium Maldovar... And of course River Song – whose secret is about to be revealed. Once that happens, nothing will ever be the same for Amy and Rory. Or for the Doctor.

But for now the adventures continue. For now, there are dangers to face, enemies to vanquish, injustices to put right and fears to be overcome. Whether it's Daleks or Cybermen, giant peg-dolls or living synthetic Flesh, the mysterious Silence or the sinister Kovarian, the Doctor and his friends will stand against the darkness, enjoy the wonders of the universe and very probably spend a lot of time running. Running for their lives – and the lives of everyone else.

Can the Doctor cheat death once again, despite everything, despite what Amy, Rory and River have seen? They can be sure of one thing – if anyone can, then it's the Doctor. The adventure isn't over yet...

ELEVEN THINGS YOU DIDN'T KNOW ABOUT
THE ELEVENTH DOCTOR

1 The Eleventh Doctor is 909 years old and may live until he is 1103.

2 The Eleventh Doctor escaped from the Tower of London in a home-made hot air balloon.

3 With the help of the TARDIS, the Doctor can understand almost every language — including baby talk.

4 The Eleventh Doctor believes he wouldn't be the Doctor any more if he did something really terrible — such as kill a beautiful, defenceless creature like a Star Whale. He'd have to find a new name.

5 The Doctor once lost a bet with Casanova and owes him a chicken.

6 The Doctor plumbed his brain into the core of an entire planet just so he could halt its orbit — and win a bet!

7 Although he seems optimistic and enthusiastic, the character of the Dream Lord — a dark aspect of the Doctor's own character — points to a deep sadness hidden within...

8 The Doctor learned to cook in Paris in the 18th century. Probably. But he still can't make a decent meringue.

9 The Eleventh Doctor claims that he can regenerate 507 times. But can he?

10 The Doctor died at Lake Silencio on 22 April 2011 at 5.02p.m.

11 One thing you must never ever do with the Eleventh Doctor is put him in a trap!

Did You Know...?

DID YOU KNOW THAT AMY AND RORY ARE THE FIRST MARRIED COUPLE TO JOIN THE DOCTOR ON HIS ADVENTURES IN THE TARDIS? HERE ARE TEN OTHER TOP FACTS YOU MIGHT NOT KNOW ABOUT THE HAPPY COUPLE:

Amy and Rory have known each other since they were children.

When they were younger, Amy used to make Rory dress up and pretend to be the 'Raggedy Doctor' in their games.

For a while before they got married, Rory was an Auton replica made of plastic.

Amy and Rory's daughter Melody is the first ever 'TARDIS baby'.

When he was an Auton, Rory killed Amy.

For a while after they got married, Amy wasn't really Amy at all, but a doppelgänger made from synthetic flesh.

One of the first things Amy and Rory did after they got married was to save the Doctor.

As the Lone Centurion, Rory waited thousands of years for Amy.

As she showed in the Dream Lord's world, Amy would rather die than live without Rory.

Rory has 'died' twice during his adventures with Amy and the Doctor – in the Dream Lord's nightmare version of Leadworth, and escaping from the Silurians.

THE REAL APOLLO MISSIONS

Space experts at NASA (which stands for National Aeronautics and Space Administration) carried out the Apollo missions in the 1960s and 70s. Their aim was to land a man on the moon – something that many people thought would be impossible!

The most famous of the Apollo missions was the *Apollo 11* space flight. This trip into space led to a human stepping out onto the moon's surface for the first time – a historic and amazing moment. The whole world wanted to know about it.

On 16 July 1969, three astronauts – Commander Neil Armstrong, 'Buzz' Aldrin and Michael Collins – blasted into space in a rocket called *Columbia* from Cape Kennedy in Florida, USA. Four days later, on 20 July, they were ready to land on the moon.

APOLLO 11

Collins stayed in orbit around the moon in *Columbia* while Armstrong and Aldrin dropped down onto the surface in a special landing craft called the *Eagle*. The astronauts spent a day on the moon, taking pictures, filming their trip, looking back at Earth and collecting rock samples. Their journey made history, and their names will always be remembered.

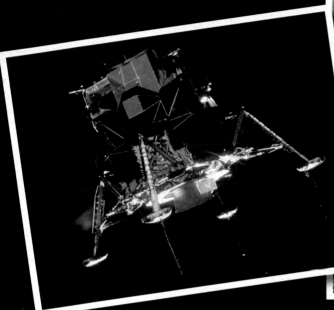

Neil Armstrong was the first human to set foot on the surface. "That's one small step for man," he said as he touched the dusty grey ground, "one giant leap for mankind."

American President Richard Nixon, along with millions of people on Earth, watched live video footage of Armstrong's amazing first steps on the moon from the White House in Washington.

Only six of the Apollo missions made it to the moon — and *Apollo 17*, in 1972, was the last time man actually landed there.

THE IMPOSSIBLE ASTRONAUT

The Doctor discovered that the reason man went to space in the first place was all because of parasite aliens called the Silence.

The nightmare creatures wanted an incredibly strong astronaut suit to protect a special young girl, so they were responsible for influencing a whole space mission as a result!

The Silence were everywhere on Earth for a long time but no one could ever remember seeing them because of their ability to edit themselves out of people's memories.

In order to save Earth from the Silence, the Doctor transmitted video footage of a Silent saying, 'You should kill us all on sight,' to the entire world while they were watching the first moon landing. This footage is shown again and again throughout history, so every time people see it they will get a warning to destroy the strange creatures.

Earth people will not remember the order given, but they will never stop obeying it.

The Silence

RECURRING NIGHTMARES

SOME MONSTERS REFUSE TO STAY AWAY. JUST WHEN YOU THINK THE UNIVERSE IS SAFE, CERTAIN HORRORS ARE KNOWN TO REAPPEAR WHEN YOU LEAST EXPECT IT.

IT IS WORTH REMEMBERING THAT EACH TIME THEY RETURN, THEY CAN BE BIGGER, BETTER, STRONGER AND USUALLY EVEN ANGRIER THAN EVER BEFORE.

GET READY TO MEET THE MONSTERS THAT COULD BE BACK FOR MORE...

DALEKS

These scary, cased creatures are the Doctor's oldest and most powerful enemy. The Doctor thought the Daleks were wiped out in the Great Time War, but has since discovered many survived.

Originally from the now destroyed planet Skaro, they have returned to fight the Doctor more times than any other monster.

Horrifically, the mutated blobs inside the strong cases used to look like us. They were the result of experiments conducted by a dangerous scientist called Davros.

When the Doctor met them again recently, he witnessed the creation of a new super race of pure Daleks and they escaped before they could be destroyed.

WARNING:
DALEKS NEVER GIVE UP. YOU WILL DEFINITELY HEAR THEIR WAR CRY 'EXTERMINATE!' AGAIN. WHEN YOU DO, MAKE SURE YOU RUN FOR YOUR LIFE.

CYBERMEN

Like the Daleks, the powerful Cybermen were once humanoid and looked like us. The original Cybermen came from Earth's twin planet Mondas, and tried to invade our world when theirs was dying. Cybermen do not need emotions, so have had these removed. All that remains of their human form is the brain.

There are Cybermen scattered throughout the universe, and their steel suits have changed several times. One thing remains though — their determination to destroy, conquer and convert people into new Cybermen.

While on a parallel Earth, the Doctor encountered a different race of Cybermen. These super-strong Cybermen turned on their creator and upgraded him to be a Cyberman, too. They also have one clear and simple plan — to make sure everyone becomes like them. Failing that, they will 'delete' you.

SONTARANS

The Sontarans might be short, but they are incredibly dangerous and are bred for one thing – war. These cloned creatures have been fighting another race called the Rutans for thousands of years. They don't get tired easily and the Doctor has run into them many times.

This alien race from the planet Sontar is notoriously powerful. They once tried to turn Earth into a Sontaran breeding planet, but thankfully the Doctor was able to stop them.

SILURIANS

The warrior Silurians are reptile creatures that lived on Earth long before humans did. They went into hibernation millions of years ago but on at least two occasions were woken up by humans by accident.

Of course, when they woke they were surprised to see how their world had changed and wanted their planet back.

The whole Silurian race is still waiting deep beneath the ground… so let's be careful not to wake them again. Ssshhh. Start drilling into the Earth and you might disturb them.

AUTONS

The Autons are creatures made from living plastic. They are controlled by the Nestene Consciousness and have attacked Earth several times.

Plastic becomes deadly around the Nestene – so look out for shop window dummies and be careful when you next open your wheelie bin!

SLITHEEN

The Family Slitheen come from a planet with one of the longest names ever – Raxacoricofallapatorius. They have clever technology that allows them to squeeze into a human skin, so they can be difficult to spot.

One Slitheen met the Doctor a couple of times, and Slitheen have also caused trouble for the Doctor's old friend, Sarah Jane Smith.

OOD

Although they're not officially dangerous, the telepathic Ood can be taken over very easily and when they are, they can be horrific and deadly! They were once used as servants for the human race — until the Doctor helped free them.

If you ever see an Ood with red eyes, there's bound to be trouble.

WEEPING ANGELS

Known as the Lonely Assassins, the Weeping Angels look like stone statues and are definitely creatures from your worst nightmare. If they are seen, they become stuck as stone statues. But when someone looks away or blinks, the Angels can move incredibly quickly, and will either zap their victim into the past or kill them instantly.

HOW TO STAY SAFE?
DON'T BLINK...

Who do you think the Doctor will meet again soon?

Put a tick beside any monsters that you think could be back next year.

◆ DALEKS

◆ CYBERMEN

◆ SONTARANS

◆ SILURIANS

◆ AUTONS

◆ SLITHEEN

◆ OOD

◆ WEEPING ANGELS

Why do you think they will return?

_____

_____

_____

_____

_____

_____

_____

_____

'TWAS THE NIGHT BEFORE CHRISTMAS...

...WHEN ALL 'ROUND THE HOUSE...

THE HOUSE OF LIGHTS

...STRANGE CREATURES WERE STIRRING.

MERRY CHRISTMAS

DING DONG

WHA - WHO?!

HELLOOO! I'M RORY, THIS IS AMY.

WE'RE SANITY INSPECTORS. YOU DO KNOW IT'S *JULY*, DON'T YOU?

YES BUT... WELL, IN *MY* HOUSE EVERY NIGHT IS CHRISTMAS EVE. IT'S THE WAY I LIKE IT. WHAT DO YOU WANT?

DON'T MIND US. ISN'T DOING CHRISTMAS 365 TIMES A YEAR A BIT, UM, WEIRD?

I KNOW THE NEIGHBOURS THINK I'M *ECCENTRIC*, BUT –

OH, I WOULDN'T WORRY ABOUT THE NEIGHBOURS...

...THEY'VE BEEN ABDUCTED BY ALIENS AND YOU'RE THE ONLY PERSON LEFT IN THIS VILLAGE.

HELLO, I'M THE DOCTOR AND YOU ARE ONE VERY LUCKY BIG OBSESSIVE FAN OF CHRISTMAS.

ALIENS? WHAT... WHAT ALIENS?

NASTY BUNCH CALLED *SCEADU*. MY GUESS IS THEY'VE TAKEN THE VILLAGERS BECAUSE THEY'RE *HUNTING* SOMETHING.

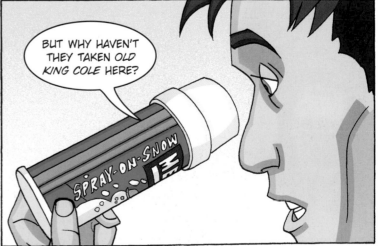

BUT WHY HAVEN'T THEY TAKEN *OLD KING COLE* HERE?

SPRAY-ON-SNOW

COS HE'S CLEVER AND HE DOESN'T KNOW IT! THING ABOUT *SCEADU* IS THEY'RE MADE OF *ANTI-PHOTONS*, WHICH ONLY EXIST PHYSICALLY IN THE *DARK*, SO...?

SO THEY CAN'T GET NEAR THIS HOUSE BECAUSE OF THE TWINKLING!

BINGO PONDO! WE'RE *COMPLETELY SAFE* IN HERE...

...AS LONG AS WE'VE GOT ALL THESE LOVELY, LIVELY, LIFE-SAVING...

FZZZZ

...LIGHTS. OH.

THEY'LL GET IN! THEY'LL GET IN HERE!

RORY, POP THESE GOGGLES ON. IT'S NIGHT VISION TIME!

ER, RIGHT, HOW DO I...?

KKRAAASH!!

AAAARGH!

QUICK, YOUNG LADY, INTO THE BASEMENT!

BUT I CAN'T LEAVE RORY AND THE DOCTOR!

KLIK

I'VE GOT A GENERATOR HOOKED UP TO THE LIGHTS DOWN HERE. AND OVER THERE IS...

WE CAN'T JUST LEAVE THEM!

WE CAN'T SAVE THEM EITHER! NOTHING CAN STOP THE SCEADU, DARKLING HORDE OF THE SUNLESS SPACE!

SINCE WHEN ARE YOU AN EXPERT ON ALIENS?

AH. WELL, YOU SEE...

...I SORT OF AM ONE.

VWIP!

The TARDIS Archives

THE DOCTOR AND HIS TARDIS ARE TELEPATHICALLY LINKED, AND AFTER THE DESTRUCTIVE REGENERATION OF THE TENTH DOCTOR, THE TARDIS RECONFIGURED ITS INTERIOR TO MATCH THE PERSONALITY OF THE ELEVENTH. TWISTING CORRIDORS AND BRANCHING STAIRWELLS REFLECT THE DOCTOR'S WANDERING MIND AND THE COLLAGE OF CONTROLS AND GADGETS ON HIS CHRISTMAS-TREE CONSOLE SUIT HIS ABSENT-MINDED EXCITEMENT AT REDISCOVERING THE UNIVERSE WITH HIS NEW COMPANIONS.

BUT NOT EVERY REDECORATION TOOK PLACE IN SUCH DRASTIC CIRCUMSTANCES. THE DOCTOR HAS CHANGED THE 'DESKTOP THEME' OF THE TARDIS SEVERAL TIMES DURING HIS LONG LIFE.

The First Doctor's TARDIS

The first Doctor's pursuit of scientific knowledge was reflected in the initial design of his TARDIS. White and clinical, the ship was more like a laboratory than a home. The few items of furniture he had dotted around the control room looked out of place next to the space age beds and equipment that lined the walls and rooms around them.

The central six-sided console, as always, dominated the control room. It was covered in levers and dials and illuminated by a huge, mirrored glass light from above — a feature that returned in the Eleventh Doctor's TARDIS.

The Secondary Control Room

Looking for a change of scenery, the Fourth Doctor stumbled upon the Secondary Control Room during a wander through the depths of the TARDIS. Smaller and wood-panelled, this control room was more Victorian in its appeal and suited the Doctor's image of himself as an almost Victorian-style adventurer.

More primitive than the main control room, the wooden hexagonal console looked more like a writing desk than a means of piloting the ship across the universe!

The Fifth Doctor's TARDIS

Whilst the features of the control room changed to become more minimal throughout the Doctor's incarnations, the main console remained very much the same as the First Doctor's TARDIS. But during the course of his incarnation he replaced the levers and dials of the console with rows upon rows of computer keyboards. These were punctuated by screens, which displayed data and information about the TARDIS' internal systems and its surroundings.

THE ZERO ROOM

Instrumental in helping the Fifth Doctor recover from his traumatic regeneration, the Zero Room provided a place of calm and tranquility. It was cut off from all outside interference to allow for peaceful meditation and even smelt of roses! Sadly, the Zero Room was deleted and converted into energy to help the TARDIS escape the massive gravitational force of the Big Bang.

The Eighth Doctor's TARDIS

As the Doctor neared the end of his seventh incarnation, the TARDIS changed to reflect his advancing years. A more sophisticated traveller than in his younger days, the Doctor surrounded himself with relics of his previous adventures. These were housed inside a huge, cathedral-like space filled with bookshelves, gantries and flickering candles. The TARDIS console remained in pride of place at the centre of the room, but its crystalline central column was now connected to the ceiling — a feature that would remain in all of the TARDIS' future incarnations so far. The wooden control panels hid their complex technology beneath polished levers and vintage dials.

Sadly, the Seventh Doctor's regeneration prevented him from truly settling into his new home, but the Eighth Doctor's gentle elegance seemed perfectly suited to the luxurious new decor.

THE EYE OF HARMONY

It was during the Eighth Doctor's first adventure that the source of the TARDIS' power was first revealed. The massive, leaf-strewn Cloister Room housed a link to the Eye of Harmony — a black hole stored in the centre of Gallifrey that generated the massive amounts of energy required by the Time Lords' civilisation.

The Ninth Doctor's TARDIS

At some point during the horrors of the Time War, the TARDIS' more homely atmosphere was replaced with a functional, more durable interior. Exposed piping and metal gantries lined the edges of the rough-textured walls, and great coral ribs provided extra reinforcement around the, now circular, central console. Gone were the elegant buttons and levers of previous consoles. Instead, the textured glass panels were littered with an assortment of gadgets and objects the Doctor had gathered on his travels. These were reused and repurposed to aid the Ninth Doctor in piloting his erratic ship more precisely.

THE TARDIS WARDROBE

When we first saw the Doctor's wardrobe it resembled a large, white walk-in cupboard, filled with outfits and garments for both himself and his companions. But as the Doctor's adventures continued, so did his collection, until eventually he had to redesign the wardrobe to contain them all. The Tenth Doctor's wardrobe was many floors tall, with a winding spiral staircase running through the centre and the clothes arranged around it.

THE HATSTAND

Whilst TARDIS interiors come and go, one item of furniture has remained constant throughout every redesign – a hatstand! This battered piece of wooden furnishing sits near the main doors to the ship and has held coats, scarves and hats from every one of the Doctor's incarnations.

'DO FISH HAVE FINGERS?'

The patchwork girl who was bigger inside than out!

Like Uncle, Auntie and Nephew, Idris was a creation of House, the sentient planet that fed on the processed energy of TARDISes. A patchwork person in a raggedy dress, her body was 'repaired' with the body parts of dead travellers. She was sacrificed to provide a safe vessel for an extracted TARDIS Matrix. But the end of her life was only the beginning of her adventures with the Doctor.

As the TARDIS was lured outside of the universe to a junkyard filled with the wreckage of ships that had gone before, its Matrix was removed so that House could feed safely on the processed Rift energy of the time and space machine. The mind of the TARDIS was supposed to burn up and die inside of the young woman's body, but Idris had other ideas.

Embracing her newfound body and soul, Idris immediately went in search of her thief – the Time Lord who had stolen her to see the universe! It took the Doctor a while to recognise his ship in human form, but when he did he was overjoyed to be able to speak to his faithful travelling companion after so long.

Together they developed a plan to create their own TARDIS console from the wreckage in the junkyard, and rescue Amy and Rory from their torture at the hands of House.

But their relationship was over before it began and Idris' human body was unable to contain a being as complex and powerful as the TARDIS forever. After draining her energy to power the makeshift console into the heart of the Doctor's old control room, Idris died for a second time and the TARDIS Matrix was restored to the ship. The Doctor might never be able to speak with her again, but at least now he knows he's in safe hands!

◆ A TARDIS doesn't experience time in order, and Idris knew things that hadn't happened yet!

◇ Idris revealed that she had archived all the Doctor's previous control rooms without him knowing, along with the controls rooms from his future.

◇ Idris considered Rory 'the pretty one.'

◆ Idris explained that although she rarely took the Doctor where he wanted to go, she always took him where he needed to go!

Letter Home

Amy has sent her parents a letter from her honeymoon with Rory. She hasn't mentioned the monsters they've met, but there are seven hidden in her words. The first one is highlighted to help you out – can you find six more?

Dear Mum and Dad,

Hello from space! Rory and I are having a blast on our honeymoon. The Doctor is really spoiling us. We've been all over and done all sorts. We visited the rainforest of Tlso Nta, ran the Nyaktar Sprint (which is really just a cosmic wheelbarrow race, though of course the Doctor is having none of it), been chariot racing with the real Cleopatra, Xi River fishing with Royal Orient Princess Mei Xie in the year 3211, tried Zero Grav Tae Kwon Do and Judo on the Orbit Dojo. We've just spent a restful weekend at the Lunar Dale Keep and Resort to recover!

We did have a bit of an accident when the Doctor let me take control of the TARDIS... we might have just nicked a heavy mining craft... and backed up the entire Translunar highway. Rory was so official; he just told everyone we could deal with the details of the prang elsewhere, and that was that. No harm done. Well, not much.

Rory's been really great actually. He's always been great, but since the whole centurion episode he's had this really positive, honest energy about him. I know I've picked a winner!

Well, I've got to dash. The Doctor is letting Rory steer us to the Aubrey Clancy-Berma Nightcruiser; a pleasure ship with cracking views of Alpha Centauri, in the year 1,000,000! How cool is that?

Love you loads,

Amy xx

The Intergalactic
BOOK of RECORDS

Believe the unbelievable!

LONGEST ARGUMENT WITH THEMSELVES:

The Aplan President on the topic of self-marriage (two heads aren't always better than one!)

MOST IDENTICAL CHILDREN:

The Sontarans – their clone worlds produce hatchings of over one million

MOST TARDISES EATEN:

House – a lot

LONGEST UNINTERRUPTED SLEEP:

The Silurians – fifty-six million years

MOST EFFICIENT USE OF SPACE:

The TARDIS – dimensionally transcendental

LEAST WELL-KNOWN ALIEN SPECIES:

The Silence – they're easily forgotten

MOST ALIEN RACES ENSLAVED:

The Daleks – countless 'inferior' species have suffered at their hands

SHORTEST-LIVED PRIME MINISTER:

Harold Saxon – a few days in office, although some people talk of a year that never was

LONGEST ENGAGEMENT:

Amy Pond and Rory Williams – approximately two thousand years

BEST PAINTING OF AN INVISIBLE CREATURE:

Vincent van Gogh – *The Church at Auvers*

LARGEST RESCUE BY A SINGLE CREATURE:

The Star Whale rescued the entire population of the UK because it couldn't bear to hear the children cry

LARGEST ALIEN RACE CREATED BY A SINGLE PERSON:

The Daleks – by Davros

RACE MOST LIKELY TO BE MISTAKEN FOR VAMPIRES:

The Saturnynes – makes you wonder what could be so bad it doesn't actually mind you thinking it's a vampire

LARGEST PARADOX:

The invasion of the Toclafane – slaughtering their own past with the help of the Doctor's butchered TARDIS

BEST IMPRESSIONIST:

Prisoner Zero – although it never quite mastered voices!

RACE MOST LIKELY TO BE ENSLAVED:

The Ood – without their hind-brains they're eager to obey

LONGEST STARE:

The Weeping Angels – their stony gaze means that they're always the last to blink!

ALIEN MADE FROM A SINGLE SUBSTANCE:

The Autons – controlled by the Nestene Consciousness, they are solid plastic

LEAST EMOTIONAL RACE:

The Cybermen – their emotional inhibitors make them ruthless killers

EARLIEST WRITING:

"Hello Sweetie" – Carved into the diamond cliffs of Planet One

Word Swirl

Solve the clues to fill in the spiral, using the last letter of each word as the first letter of the next.

2.

3.

4.

1.

11.

5.

8.

9.

10.

7.

6.

1. An ancient prison built to hold the Doctor
2. The name of the first US space mission to land on the moon
3. When the Doctor meets Nephew at the junkyard, what kind of alien is he?
4. The Doctor's greatest enemy
5. This invisible creature plagued Vincent van Gogh
6. This lonely giant helped the UK in its hour of need

7. The number of regenerations the Doctor has undergone so far
8. The controlling force behind the Autons
9. An alternative name for Homo Reptilia
10. These aliens wipe themselves from the memories of those who see them
11. The aliens that inhabited old people in the nightmare created by the Dream Lord

THE SILENCE

'SILENCE WILL FALL.'

THE ESCAPED PRISONER ZERO TALKED OF THE SILENCE, BUT THE DOCTOR, AMY AND RORY DID NOT FIND OUT WHAT THIS MEANT FOR A VERY LONG TIME...

The Silence came to Earth thousands of years ago — and got everywhere. This race is one of the scariest species that the Doctor has ever encountered. Made up of horrific, bulbous-headed creatures, these monsters are masters of self-defence.

The Silence are memory proof. As soon as you look away from them they edit themselves out of your memory. You might have bumped into one, but you will not remember. And if you did make a note of seeing the creature while you were looking at it, you would still forget what it looked like after you turned away.

The Silence gets other life forms to do all the hard work for them, influencing human behaviour so that they get what they want.

They do not need weapons — why would they, when no one can ever remember seeing them?

TAKE A LOOK AT THIS PAGE FOR A LONG TIME — WRITE DOWN A DESCRIPTION SOMEWHERE IN CASE YOU FORGET WHAT YOU HAVE JUST READ WHEN YOU TURN OVER TO THE NEXT PAGE...

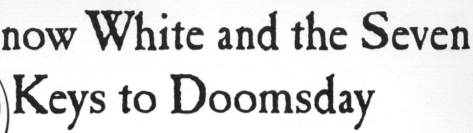Snow White and the Seven Keys to Doomsday

Once upon a time, long long ago in the Old Times when Gallifrey was young, Rassilon set up the Matrix and was made first President of the Time Lords. And to be sure that none would challenge his rule, or threaten the safety and harmony of the Time Lords, Rassilon asked the Matrix a question.

He stood in the Great Hall of Time, where a portal to the Matrix hung above the debating table, and he asked the Matrix:

'Matrix, Matrix that sees over all, who has the power to make Gallifrey fall?'

And the Matrix replied: 'Only you, oh Rassilon. Only you, through the Eye of Harmony have that power.'

Each and every day, Rassilon asked the same question.

Each and every day he received the same reply.

Until, one day, the Matrix replied: 'Snowana the Fair, using the Keys of Doomsday, she has the power to destroy all of Gallifrey.'

Rassilon was enraged by this response, and summoned the High Council of all Time Lords. They met for many hours in the Panopticon, to decide the fate of Swowana. Some argued that she must be vaporised, others that she was only a young girl not yet even attending the Academy, and that the Matrix must be wrong.

But Rassilon knew that the Matrix was never wrong. And with sorrow and with heavy hearts, he banished the girl into the wastelands of Outer Gallifrey, where she could do no harm and would surely die. So that he would never be faced with a similar decision, Rassilon never asked the Matrix the question again.

But Snowana did not die. She was a brave and clever child and survived on fruits and berries, sheltering from the sun and the wind. She found other 'Outlers' living outside the Citadel of Gallifrey, and over the years Snowana grew into a beautiful woman. The Outlers called her Snow White, because her skin was so pale as she kept out of the sun.

One of the Outlers was a handsome man named Selendor, and he fell in love with Snow White. But she did not love him, for she knew he was a cruel and selfish man who had escaped to Outer Gallifrey after murdering his own brother and father. So she rejected his love, and that made Selendor even more angry. Ever since he left, Selendor had been intent on revenge. He blamed Rassilon and the Time Lords for his crime, and for his self-imposed exile, and he was determined to destroy Gallifrey and bring the Time Lords to their knees.

Digging deep in the ground, Selendor discovered a powerful ore which he mined and fashioned into an awesome weapon. He created a terrible machine, and from the refined ore he made seven keys, one for each of the 'crimes' of the Time Lords of Gallifrey. There was a Key of Pride, and a Key of Injustice. There was a Key of Power and a Key of Exile. There was a Key of Knowledge and a Key of Wisdom. And last and greatest of all, there was the Key of Nevermore.

When his machine and its keys were complete, Seledor called the Outlers together and he told them of his plan to bring Doomsday to the world. Even though they were outcasts themselves, they begged him to reconsider, but he refused. He started to insert the keys into the machine, and as its terrible power grew, the Outlers fled and hoped to find safety.

All except Snow White, who begged Selendor not to destroy the world. She lied to him, and said that he was all the world to her. If he would not stop, then he should at least let her use the last key to have her own revenge. Knowing that Snow White had been unfairly banished by Rassilon, Selendor gave her the Key of Nevermore, sure that she would use it.

And so it was that the Matrix was proved right. Snow White who had been Snowana held the Key of Nevermore, and with it she had the power to make Gallifrey fall.

But instead of using that power, she took the Key of Nevermore, and she ran from Selendor and hid. He sought her through the wastelands, and she knew that one day he would find her. She could not destroy the Key, and so she used her knowledge to fashion herself a place of safety. She used the power of the Key to blend force fields together and create a box. And she lay in the force field box, and was safe from all the world and the Key was safe with her for none could break into the box without destroying the power of the Key.

After seven years, Selendor found her, as if dead inside what appeared to be a glass coffin. And he wept for the loss of his love. But the love he wept for losing was not Snow White but the Key of Nevermore and the end of Gallifrey. It is said that he wept until he had no more tears, and still he wept until he passed away from grief and Seledor the Destroyer was no more.

But Snow White slept on, one of the Seven Keys of Doomsday clutched to her hearts.

Some say she is sleeping still.

The End

The Doctionary

The Doctor has a habit of letting his sentences run away from him and often forgets what he's talking about himself. But when it comes to life-threatening situations, understanding what the Doctor's talking about can mean the difference between living and dying.

What the Doctor says: "You know when grown-ups tell you everything's going to be fine, and you think they're probably lying to make you feel better...? Everything's going to be fine."

What the Doctor means:

Everything is **NOT** going to be fine.

What the Doctor says: "Well I'm not now, but I was back then. Well back now, from your point of view, which is back then from my point of view — time travel, you can't keep it straight in your head."

But you're not in the Pandorica.

What the Doctor means:

I'm here from the future.

What the Doctor says: "A big flashy lighty thing — that's what brought me here. Big flashy lighty things have got me written all over them. Not actually. But give me time and a crayon. Now can anyone tell me what this big flashy lighty thing does? No you can't, cos it's still my go! This big flashy lighty thing is connected to the spire on your dome, yeah? And it controls the sky. Well technically it controls the clouds, which technically aren't clouds at all. Well, they're clouds of tiny particles of ice. Ice clouds, love that!"

What the Doctor means:

Can I take a look at your Sky-Mast Weather Controller please?

What the Doctor says: "You've completely won. You could kill us in oodles of really inventive ways. So. Yeah. Right. But. Before you do kill us. Let me — and my friends Amy and Rory — congratulate you on being a truly worthy opponent."

What the Doctor means:

Start running, because you've lost.

What the Doctor says: "It may have been the grit in Ernie's heart as he fried to the sound of German bombers screaming towards York, but that night produced the best fish supper EVER in the history of the world. I'll drop you off. Take your time. Don't rush."

What the Doctor means:

I need some space.

What the Doctor says: "Time isn't a straight line, it's all bumpy-wumpy. There's loads of boring stuff — like Sundays and Tuesdays and Thursday afternoons — but now and then there are Saturdays! Big temporal tipping points when anything's possible! The TARDIS can't resist them — like a moth to a flame, she loves a party."

What the Doctor means:

I don't think the TARDIS is listening to where I'm telling her to go.

What the Doctor says: "Safe? No, of course you're not safe. There's about a billion other things out there, just waiting to burn your whole world. But if you want to pretend you're safe, just so you can sleep at night, okay, you're safe. But you're not really."

What the Doctor means:

Good luck!

What the Doctor says: "D'you know, there's a thing called a face spider, it's just like a tiny baby's head with spider legs, and it's specifically evolved to scuttle around at the backs of bedroom cupboards..."

What the Doctor means:

Shall we hide in this cupboard?

ATTACK OF THE 50 FT RORY

TWO HOURS EARLIER.

EEEEOOOOEEEEE

DOCTOR! WHAT IS THAT?!

WHAT DOES IT SOUND LIKE?

EEEEOOOOEEEEE

THE WORST CAR ALARM IN THE UNIVERSE?

THAT'S AN INTERGALACTIC SOS - SOMEONE NEEDS URGENT HELP...

WHAT'S THE PROBLEM THEN?

RAT!

I MUST REMEMBER TO CHECK THE SCANNER!

OVER HERE!

WHAT DO YOU RECKON? GIANT RAT EATS GIANT ANT?

GIANT ANT EATS GIANT RAT?

NEITHER. I THINK THEY'D BOTH PREFER US!

SO I THINK WE KNOW WHAT THE DISTRESS SIGNAL WAS ALL ABOUT.

BUT WHO SENT IT?

AT A GUESS I'D SAY PROFESSOR FINN OF THE HOPE INSTITUTE OF SCIENCE.

WHO?

HIS NAME'S ON THE DOOR.

PROFESSOR FINN HOPE INSTITUTE OF SCIENCE

I THINK I NEED TO TALK TO HIM.

RORY, DISTRACT THE GIANTS.

WHAT?

MY HUSBAND IS NOT A DECOY.

SOMEBODY'S GOT TO DO IT. IF IT'S NOT RORY THEN YOU'LL HAVE TO.

RORY - DISTRACT THE GIANTS.

HOW?

YOU'LL THINK OF SOMETHING.

NOW.

THAT MACHINE MUST BE SOME KIND OF INSTANT GROWTH RAY.

BUT CAN IT BE REVERSED?

GET OFF!

RORY! PUT ME DOWN.

RORY!

I DON'T THINK HE CAN HEAR YOU.

WHY NOT? HIS EARS ARE BIG ENOUGH.

I THINK THE SHOCK OF GROWING SUDDENLY HAS AFFECTED HIS BRAIN. YOU HAVE TO GET HIM TO REMEMBER WHO HE IS OR WE'LL NEVER CHANGE HIM BACK.

DON'T LEAVE ME DOCTOR!

JUST GET HIM TO REMEMBER...

LISTEN TO ME. YOU'RE RORY WILLIAMS, YOU'VE GOT TO REMEMBER. IT'S ME AMY. THE GIRL WITH THE IMAGINARY FRIEND WHO WASN'T IMAGINARY AT ALL.

REMEMBER THE ATRAXI, THOSE VAMPIRES IN VENICE, THE SILURIAN CITY, THE PANDORICA... HOW COULD YOU FORGET OUR HONEYMOON?

WAS THERE ANYTHING ELSE WITH THIS WHEN YOU FOUND IT?

ONLY ANOTHER OF THESE CRYSTAL PYRAMID THINGS. I THOUGHT IT WAS A SPARE.

WHERE IS IT?

IT'S IN HERE SOMEWHERE. AH!

HERE YOU ARE.

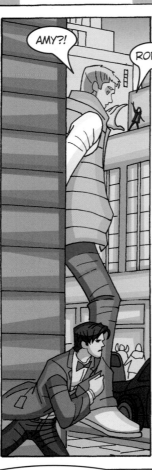

AMY?!

RORY!

NOW I RECOGNISE WHAT THESE ARE. THEY WERE DEVELOPED BY A WARRIOR RACE FROM DEHLIOP FOUR.

THE DEHLIOPS WERE A LOT SMALLER THAN MOST OF THEIR NEIGHBOURS AND CREATED THIS TECHNOLOGY TO MAKE THEM BIGGER. BUT THEY NEVER PERFECTED IT; IT HAD UNFORTUNATE SIDE-EFFECTS...

IT WAS USED FOR WAR?

NOW WE CAN FINISH THE JOB.

LIKE LOSING YOUR MIND!

EXACTLY. FINALLY THE MACHINES WERE BANNED. THIS ONE MUST HAVE BEEN SMUGGLED OFF OF DEHLIOP BEFORE IT COULD BE DESTROYED.

RIGHT LET'S FIND A SUN TO DROP THOSE THINGS INTO... UNLESS YOU WANT TO KEEP IT. WE COULD SORT OUT THAT NOSE OF YOURS.

WHAT'S WRONG WITH MY NOSE?

ABSOLUTELY NOTHING. YOU'RE PERFECT JUST THE SIZE YOU ARE.

THE END

DOUBLE TROUBLE

The Doctor has bumped into several doubles in his long life – including many of himself! It can make life confusing at times, and almost definitely always means trouble. Especially when you don't know who is the real version and who is the double...

GANGERS

Wouldn't it be useful if you could make a copy of yourself to do all the jobs you don't want to do – you know, like homework or tidying up your bedroom? In the 22nd century, humans have a similar idea and they create the Flesh.

The Flesh can be used to create an exact replica of another person – right down to their memories and clothes. Humans call these copies 'Gangers', as in doppelgänger, meaning a double of a living person.

Controlled by their human equivalent, the Ganger does all the dangerous jobs so that the human controlling it doesn't get hurt. If the Ganger's body is injured, it is just melted down and a new Ganger is created.

The Gangers need humans to control them – until a solar tsunami hits Earth. After that, they find they can work independently of their human doubles. And they want revenge! Luckily, a Ganger copy of the Doctor helps out. Eventually, the Doctor discovers that he and Rory are travelling in the TARDIS with a Ganger version of Amy – and the real Amy is trapped somewhere else!

DOUBLE DOCTOR!

The Flesh copy of the Doctor wasn't the first – many others have tried!

ROBOT DOCTOR DOUBLES

The Daleks once made robot versions of the First and Fifth Doctor. Sharaz Jek created an android version of the Fifth Doctor's body.

COPYCATS

The Fourth Doctor has many copies made of him! First, the monsters called the Kraals made an android version of him. A creepy cactus creature called Meglos once copied the Fourth Doctor's form and pretended to be him. Another time, the Fourth Doctor created a clone of himself to fight a monster inside his head. Finally, Prisoner Zero copied the Eleventh Doctor's body while it tried to escape capture.

LOOKS FAMILIAR?

On Earth, by coincidence, the Abbot of Amboise looked just like the First Doctor, and a politician called Salamander looked exactly like the Second Doctor.

DUPLICATE DOCTOR

The Tenth Doctor had a duplicate – made out of his spare hand and the Human DNA of his friend Donna Noble! This Doctor now lives on a parallel Earth with Rose Tyler.

MORE COPYCATS

PRISONER ZERO

This multi-form shape-changing creature escaped through a crack in Amy Pond's bedroom and copied the bodies of several people in Leadworth — including a man and his dog, a woman and her two children and little Amelia Pond.

ZYGONS

The Zygons were shape changers that came to Earth when their spaceship crashed into Loch Ness in Scotland. They took the shape of several people — including the Doctor's companion Harry — and planned to conquer Earth.

AUTONS

The living plastic creatures can easily make copies of people out of plastic. They once made a copy of Rose's old boyfriend, Mickey Smith, which attacked the Doctor and Rose in a restaurant. Sometimes though, the shiny, glowing skin can make the Auton copy stand out.

INVADING ANDROIDS

As well as making a version of the Doctor, the Kraals once made android versions of Sarah Jane Smith and her friend Harry Sullivan.

PARALLEL PEOPLE

On a parallel world, we met doubles of Rose's mum and dad and also Mickey Smith – although on this parallel world he was called Ricky.

SLITHEEN

The Raxacoricofallapatorians became doubles of important humans to trick their way into Number Ten Downing Street and set off a nuclear war. They didn't make doubles of them, but squeezed their fat bodies into special skin suits made from their victims.

CLONED COMPANION

The Sontarans created a copy of the Doctor's friend Martha Jones to help them with their deadly plans.

RORY'S ADVENTURE

It was nice to have a bit of free time. Flying through time and space having adventures was all very well, but you needed a bit of time just to relax and chill out and catch your breath, Rory thought. And Spaceport One was just the place. On the outskirts of Dorfnan City, it was a huge leisure and shopping complex as well as a spaceport. The Doctor had told Amy and Rory that they could walk the shopping streets for days and still not get to every shop.

Not that Rory was too bothered by the shops. He just fancied a break, time to sit and have coffee and a cake. Amy, of course, did want to go shopping, so Rory left her to get on with it. They agreed to meet back at the TARDIS later.

Some of the shops were interesting. Rory was fascinated by the latest electronic gadgets and gizmos. But as he was looking at a display of fingertop computers, he noticed the unmistakable smell of freshly baked bread.

The smell was coming from just a few shops away. But when Rory tracked it down, it seemed to be the back door of a bakery rather than the main entrance. Maybe he could cut through – the door was standing slightly open. Rory found himself in what seemed to be a

back office. There was a desk covered in papers – bills and invoices and stock lists. He could see a door that he hoped led through to the main shop.

But between Rory and the other door, a huge archway was set up. Cables ran from it to a junction box. The archway itself flickered and shimmered as if it wasn't really there.

Rory was staring at it in fascination when the inner door opened. Quickly, Rory hid behind the desk. He peered nervously over the top, and saw a large reptilian creature enter the room. It was wearing a baker's apron. The creature adjusted controls on the junction box, then stood in front of the archway.

The reptilian alien's voice was a throaty

growl. 'General Mystan – all is prepared. The power levels are now sufficient for transfer through the transmat gateway. As soon as I close the shop, you can order the fleet to attack and the invasion can begin. I have waited so long for this moment...' The reptilian alien gave a huge sigh, then turned and stomped from the room.

An invasion didn't sound good to Rory. He wondered if he could sabotage the transmat gateway somehow. But the controls didn't make any sense to him. Maybe he could smash it...

'Hello.'

Rory nearly jumped out of his skin. He hadn't

noticed the door opening again. A boy was standing there, watching Rory. Over the boy's shoulder, Rory could see into the shop. There were people queuing up for bread and cakes – people who would be caught in the forefront of the alien invasion.

'You shouldn't be here,' Rory hissed at the boy.

'Sorry.'

Behind the boy, Rory could see the baker turning. Any moment he would see the open door – and the boy and Rory.

But then the baker froze, staring at a pile of doughnuts on a shelf close to the counter.

'There's one missing,' he growled angrily, his voice carrying easily to where Rory and the boy were standing. 'Who's stolen a doughnut?!'

The baker turned to survey the gathered customers.

'Now's your chance,' Rory told the boy. He had to save him from being caught up in the invasion. 'Get away from here – run! It's dangerous, you have to run for it.'

The boy pulled the door shut behind him. Rory heard the shouts of the baker, and the chatter of the other customers. At least he had a few moments to try to sabotage the transmat gateway. He reached for the biggest, thickest cable and wrenched it out of the junction box.

Immediately Rory could tell this was a mistake. The transmat gateway was glowing brighter than ever. And framed within it, an army of the reptilian creatures in full battle armour faded into existence.

Rory ducked behind the desk again. 'Not good,' he murmured.

The aliens seemed confused. They looked round in surprise, more and more of them pushing through the gateway into the room.

'It is too soon,' one of the reptilian aliens announced. 'For the plan to work, our attack must be coordinated with the arrival of the invasion fleet.'

There was no way that Rory could get to either door without being spotted, so he stayed hiding behind the desk. But sooner or later, he knew, one of the aliens would notice him. His only hope was causing a distraction.

The inner door opened and the baker came in again. He stared in reptilian surprise at the invaders.

'What are you doing? General Mystan, it is too soon. I didn't activate the transmat gateway.'

But Rory was distracted by another arrival. The back door of the shop was slowly opening. As Rory watched, the boy who had been there before slipped inside. Rory waved at him frantically to leave. But the boy saw him, and crawled past the reptilians, all now intent on listening to the baker's report.

'It must have been that boy,' the baker was saying. The leading alien – General Mystan – growled angrily in response.

'I told you to get away from here,' Rory whispered to the boy as he joined Rory behind the desk.

'I did,' the boy whispered back. 'But my friend and I wanted to know what's going on.'

'An invasion's what's going on! We need a distraction so we can get out of here and raise the alarm.'

Everyone turned – including Rory and the boy as well as the alien invaders – as they heard a hammering from the front door of the shop.

'See who it is,' General Mystan ordered. 'Get rid of them.'

'That'll be my friend,' the boy whispered.

'We have to get away,' Rory whispered back to the boy. 'As soon as you see your chance, run for it. Again!'

Rory edged along, trying to get a better view of where the aliens were and which way they were looking. His foot caught on a cable, and he slipped and fell flat on his face. He couldn't help crying out. At once all the aliens turned towards Rory.

He leaped to his feet and dashed towards the back door. 'Run!' he yelled.

With the aliens turning to follow Rory, the way to the front of the shop was clear. The boy ran full pelt for the door into the bakery.

Distracted by the boy, the aliens turned again. They were large, bulky and awkward creatures, and this gave Rory a chance to get to the back door and dive through. He looked over his shoulder, but to his surprise the alien reptiles didn't seem to be following.

With a sigh of relief, Rory turned – and walked straight into what looked like an enormous upright rhinoceros in the dark leather armour of a spaceport security guard. That was why the aliens hadn't followed.

'Category – human,' the security guard rumbled. 'Produce papers.'

Rory didn't have any papers. 'There's an invasion,' he blurted out. 'These scaly alien things are invading the bakery.' He hesitated. 'Sorry – that sounds completely daft, doesn't it? But there's an invasion fleet coming, that's what their leader said. He's called General Mystan.'

The security guard took a step backwards. 'Mystan? Category – Reptilodon. Designation – enemy.' He grabbed a cylindrical communicator from his belt and spoke rapidly into it. To Rory it sounded like: 'Bo ro go so mo la te do.'

Rory followed the guard down a side alley towards the front of the bakery. Already a dozen more of the space rhino security guards were marching towards the bakery. Rory was surprised that the invaders hadn't already emerged and

started their attack.

Then he saw the boy through the bakery window. He was throwing bread and cakes and pushing over shelves to slow the attackers' advance. There was someone else with him, helping to drag the counter across the shop and block the alien advance. But Rory couldn't see them properly.

'Oh, good one!' Rory said. He was about to run to help when a heavy hand clamped down on his shoulder.

'You stay,' the security guard commanded. 'Check papers later.'

'Oh, er, right.'

As soon as the security guard joined its colleagues and marched into the bakery, Rory ran the other way. He didn't stop running until he reached the TARDIS. He might have prevented an alien invasion, and he was sorry not to say goodbye to the boy he'd met. But he didn't fancy having to explain why he didn't have the right papers or identification.

Rory had just got his breath back when Amy arrived. Rory was surprised she wasn't laden down with shopping, but she said she'd found the spaceport boring. He wondered how she had got jam in her hair, but she didn't seem keen to tell him.

Inside the TARDIS, the Doctor was leaning against the console. 'Ah, there you are. Good – all finished now and ready to go. Amy, you've got jam in your hair.'

'It has been mentioned,' she told him.

'And Rory – you look like you've had a run in with a Judoon. But then you always look like that.'

Rory wasn't listening. 'What are you eating?' he demanded.

'What this?' The Doctor held it up for them to see. 'Oh, I got finished early and felt a bit peckish so I just popped out for a doughnut.' He shoved the rest of the doughnut in his mouth and pulled a lever. 'Now,' the Doctor said indistinctly, through a mouth full of jam and cream, 'let's go somewhere more exciting this time, shall we?'

THE END

The Siren's Call

Can you avoid the lure of the Siren's call and make it safely back to the TARDIS before the Black Spot gets you?

START

HOW TO PLAY:

Roll a die to see who starts. The person to roll the highest number goes first. Players take it in turns to roll the die and move their playing pieces forward by the number of places shown. Players should then follow the instructions on the spaces they land on. The winner is the first player to reach the TARDIS.

1

2

Hide in the armoury. Move forwards one space.

24

22

21

25

26

20

BLACK SPOT! Move to the Sick Bay and miss a turn.

SICK BAY

Return to the Black Spot you came from after missing a turn.

Hear the Siren's Call. Move back two spaces.

28

29

30

31

32

34

6

BLACK SPOT! Move to the Sick Bay and miss a turn.

8

9

10

11

5

Hear the Siren's call. Move back two spaces.

13

14

Man overboard! Race forwards one space.

3

Shut below decks. Miss a turn.

16

42

41

43

17

40

BLACK SPOT! Move to the Sick Bay and miss a turn.

19

39

BLACK SPOT! Move to the Sick Bay and miss a turn.

45

Run from the Siren. Move forwards two spaces.

37

46

36

47

35

Stop for treasure. Miss a turn.

50

POLICE PUBLIC CALL BOX

49

FINISH

FIND THE FLESH

THE GANGERS ARE PRETTY STRANGE LOOKING ANYWAY, BUT THERE'S ONE IN EACH OF THESE SETS THAT IS THE ODD ONE OUT. CAN YOU SPOT THEM?

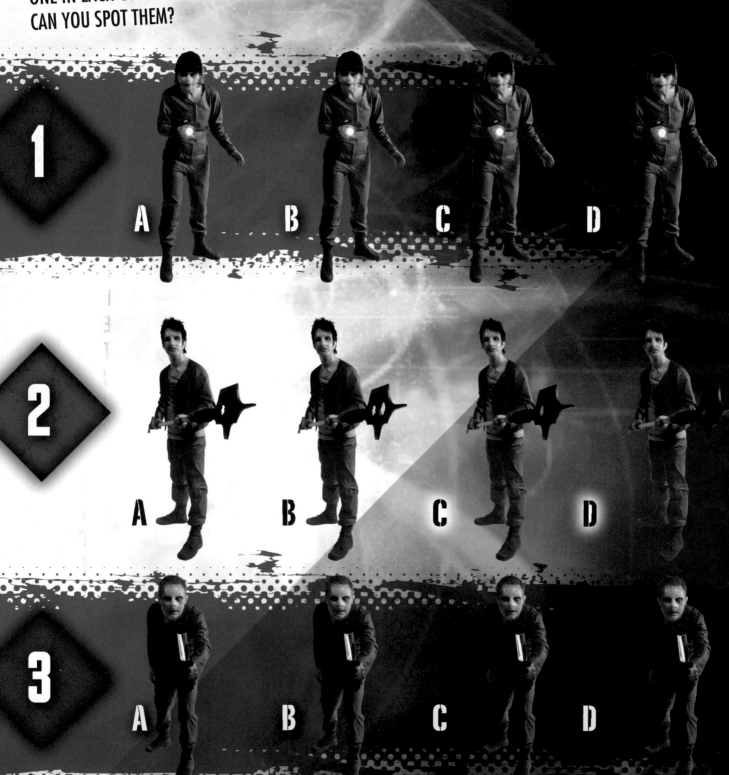

Double the Fun

Just like the Gangers, every word in this word search appears twice. Can you find all the words?

```
Q W E R T A P O L L O H J U K I O R T G M V N B G
G G N J H G F D F B H T H J O L L V F E E R T H U
H B A D F R C G T B G V C E R G M A L O P R G U J
Y G I N O O C F A N H Y T F V P L O H K I L I L T
T F R E G L E A R A F R G M E E D O C T O R O P N
F R A M H E N K D B G S S E G Y R W E R V F R T A
D E V R O I R O I S F H J L F G H P O I D R I S O
A S O E J K E S S A V B H O Y R T J K V M I K L K
D W K B S A T I Q E A B C D A Q K C L E R I C S O
C R O Y V D A R F G F E D Y R F J N V R B V C F C
Y E S C F E R E E B E G O W N N O P J S D F G H Y
E R R T Y U J N D H S Q C S Y S W B I O A S E E B
F P O H G V G A A E U A T M S U Y A U N V G H T E
G L P R V C V G H D O S A C V I V F T G O I K J R
H S L G B X F L E S H D V E R T D T R V P O I H M
T M I Q N O K J G D S C T F U O T R H B A H T R E
Y N J R B L H J C G O G K O V A R I A N V H T Q N
U B O A D W I O N V O V B G T R H A A T A G N B B
I V O B Q I Q O D F A P O L L O S T A E D F G T E
K C L C A D S A S D Y A S D F G H C V B G T T Y O
L X K D N R T A R S H H J K I U T R I R H S E L F
I D V E E R R G D F M V B N M D F F R R W I G Y D
O E R V T D O C T O R O E R T Y S D T W E S A M H
Q I I A G P R N M J I Y T S R E G N A G Z L E A P
S R S S V P Y M A R D E O H O U S E P Q R S C Y G
```

Amy	Cybermen	Gangers	Kovarian	Rory
Apollo	Doctor	House	Melody	Siren
Clerics	Flesh	Idris	River Song	TARDIS

Answers

Page 29
Postcard Home

Dear Mum and Dad,

Hello from space! Rory and I are having a blast on our honeymoon. The Doctor is really spoiling us. We've been all over and done all sorts. We visited the rainforest of Tlso Nta, ran the Nyaktar Sprint (which is really just a cosmic wheelbarrow race, though of course the Doctor is having none of it), been chariot racing with the real Cleopatra, Xi River fishing with Royal orient Princess Mei Xie in the year 3211, tried Zero Grav Tae Kwon Do and Judo on the orbit Dojo. We've just spent a restful weekend at the Lunar Dale Keep and Resort to recover!

We did have a bit of an accident when The Doctor let me take control of the TARDIS... we might have just nicked a heavy mining craft ... and backed up the entire Translunar highway. Rory was so official; he just told everyone we could deal with the details of the prang elsewhere, and that was that. No harm done. Well, not much.

Rory's been really great actually. He's always been great, but since the whole centurion episode he's had this really positive, honest energy about him. I know I've picked a winner!

Well, I've got to dash. The Doctor is letting Rory steer us to the Aubrey Clancy-Berma Nightcruiser; a pleasure ship with cracking views of Alpha Centauri, in the year 1,000,000! How cool is that?

Love you loads,

Amy xx

Page 36
Word Swirl

1. PANDORICA
2. APOLLO
3. OOD
4. DALEK
5. KRAYFAYIS
6. STARWHALE
7. ELEVEN
8. NESTENECONCIOUSNESS
9. SILURIANS
10. SILENCE
11. EKNODYNE

Page 58
Find the Flesh

1. D, 2. B, 3. C.

Page 59
Double the Fun